THE MEDIEVAL LIBRARY UNDER
THE GENERAL EDITORSHIP OF
SIR ISRAEL GOLLANCZ, Litt.D., F.B.A.

The Tumbler of Our Lady

# Of The Tumbler of Our Lady and other Miracles now Translated from the Middle French with Introduction and Notes by Alice Kemp-Welch

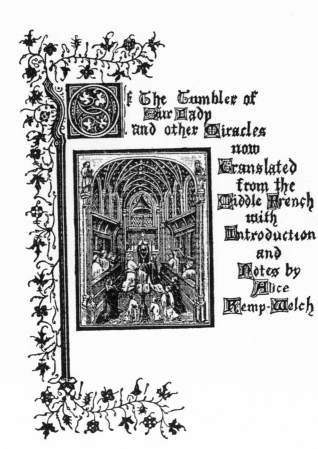

The title on the reverse of this
page, engraved upon the wood,
was designed by Miss Blanche
C. Hunter after B.M. Add.
MS. 16997, f. 145.

# OF THE TUMBLER OF OUR LADY & OTHER MIRACLES NOW TRANS-LATED FROM THE MIDDLE FRENCH : INTRODUCTION AND NOTES BY ALICE KEMP-WELCH

COOPER SQUARE PUBLISHERS, INC.
NEW YORK
1966

PQ

1534

.T4

E5

1966

Published 1966 by Cooper Square Publishers, Inc.
59 Fourth Avenue, New York, N. Y. 10003
Library of Congress Catalog Card No. 66-23319

Printed in the United States of America
by Noble Offset Printers Inc., New York, N. Y. 10003

# ILLUSTRATIONS

---

NOTE.—The plate of "The Tumbler of Our Lady" contained in this volume is photographed direct from the XIIIth Century MS., now in the *Bibliothèque de l'Arsenal*, Paris ; the remainder are reproduced after the plates in the *Edition Poquet* (1857), the Original MS. heretofore in the suppressed *Séminaire* at Soissons, being at present inaccessible to the public.

# CONTENTS

# INTRODUCTION

THE Miracles here done into English are for the most part from the collection made in the thirteenth century by Gautier de Coinci, a monk of St. Médard, near Soissons. Of this once royal abbey of the Frankish kings, the goal of many a pilgrimage, hardly a trace now remains, the crypt being all that is left of its former grandeur. The MS. which enshrines most of these delightful stories is in the Séminaire at Soissons, and is a glorious specimen of the limner's art of the thirteenth century. Each story has its appropriate illustration on a diapered background of gold, blue, and red, the whole being prefaced by a full-page illumination of surpassing beauty, such as could only have been conceived in the soul of a fervent worshipper. The stories themselves were, in the thirteenth century, translated into French from collections in Latin, the matter of which had been brought together from various sources during the eleventh and twelfth centuries, the East supplying many of the themes. In the Middle Ages, the Church felt no scruple in making use, whether for the decoration of her own sacred walls, or for the enrichment and popularisation of her teaching, of the Pagan forms which she had inherited from antiquity, but whilst adopting established forms and motives, she sanctified them by interpreting them in a Christian sense. Eastern tales were adapted to the glorification of the Holy Mother in the same spirit as Eastern Beast-lore was adapted to Christian temples and Christian moralisations. Some were brought by Crusaders, some by traders and travellers, and were fashioned to the service of religion by pious hands and simple hearts within the shelter of the cloister.

Apart from other considerations, the Miracle-stories contain much internal evidence of an Eastern origin, especially in their diffuseness and their moralisations, characteristics very dear to the Eastern and the mediæval mind alike. The lesson to be learnt is not left to be inferred, but is definitely set forth, so that " even fools cannot err therein."

Amongst these stories we can trace constant variants of the same subjects, many of which were local legends. In the centres specially dedicated to the cult of the Virgin, the same stories are to be found in two or more places, with a mere change of background, for the collectors of such material thought it not unfitting to adapt from any source anything which made for edification. Thus, for instance, we find traditions which seem properly to belong to the town of Soissons transported to Chartres or elsewhere. Communication in mediæval times was not rapid, and a marvellous story, with slight adaptations, suited one place just as well as another. By the time it became generally known, each town, forgetting or ignorant of its real origin, would claim it as its own, and then there would begin the never ending contention which has repeated itself all through history, whether it be as to the tomb of a classic hero, a Virgin miracle, or a picture by the great Leonardo da Vinci.

In France, in the Middle Ages, the cult of the Virgin formed the great religious, just as the cult of woman formed the great social, movement. Religion and chivalry joined hands. "For Our Lady," or "For God and my Lady," was the cry as men hurled themselves into the thickest of the fight. And with this close interchange of idea, a change gradually came in man's conception, the Goddess becoming humanised, the woman deified. This idea of the humanity of the Virgin became the fundamental theme of religious thought, modifying life, art, and literature. MSS., pictures, sculpture, all proclaim a tender Mother rather than a stately Queen in the Heavens. On the other hand, a regard and reverence for womanhood had developed, not merely for woman as the weaker vessel, but as the principle of all Good, and of moral elevation. How different is this position of the days of chivalry from that of the heroic days! Then, woman might be the cause of war, but it was not undertaken to please her, or to do her honour. Then, love was often treated as a weakness, an impediment, not a stimulus, to heroism. Love in the light of chivalry was a favour from heaven.

It has, however, often been objected that, in contrast with this fair picture, there is much in the literature of the Middle Ages which seems to present a different aspect. But if we examine the stories, and consider their sources and their transcribers, we shall perhaps find the reason for these distorted outlines, filled in with much imperfectly understood detail. In the first place, many of these stories came, as we have already said, from the East, and more particularly from India, and had their *raison d'être* in the land of the Zenana. Passing to the West, Eastern ideas, and Eastern exaggeration, misconstrued, became caricature. Then again, the compilers of stories were generally monks, who were incapable of judging woman with respect. Even if, in individual cases, they had been, still they were obliged to further the teaching of the Church, which had early discovered the power of woman as

well as that of music, and had taken both into her
service, subjecting the one, in both mind and body,
and making the other a part of her daily ritual.

The other principal purveyors of stories were the
minstrels, who also were, as a rule, unfitted to give any
true idea of woman.  They were, for the most part,
ignorant men who wandered from castle to castle, and
made no pretence to do more than please and amuse.
And so, except by the careful student, the grotesque
and fanciful narrations of monks and minstrels have
been accepted as real history, and the woman of the
Middle Ages has been defamed.

Turning again to the Virgin, and the later mediæval
attitude towards her, we find the idea of her humanity
revealed not only in the miracles, but also in one of
the greatest works of piety of the thirteenth century
—" The meditations on the life of Jesus Christ," of
St. Bonaventura—which, through the medium of the
" Mysteries," introduced into sacred pictorial art some
of its most dramatic and appealing scenes.  Where is
there to be found anything more tenderly human than

the incident of Christ taking leave of His Mother before His journey to Jerusalem to consummate His mission, or than the final farewell of the Holy Mother, seated at the foot of the Cross in the dying daylight, holding in her arms the dead Christ, the glowing rays of the fast sinking sun being, as it were, the counterpart of the glowing love of the grief-stricken Mother ?

It is only by entering into this spirit of human intimacy that we can in anywise appreciate what such miracle-stories meant to the simple folk of the Middle Ages, with whom religion and daily life went hand in hand. Even we ourselves, as we read them, cannot fail to be touched by their tenderness and naïveté, and by a certain charm which so pervades them, that we seem for the time to be living in the same strange intellectual and moral atmosphere.

Queen of Heaven. Such was the Virgin to St. Bernard, teaching in the twelfth century, and he entreats her " Advocata nostra."

Dante, a century later, had realised the Holy Mother, and he exclaims " In te misericordia, in te pietate."

" ON the faith of my soul, so many pleasing miracles of Our Lady do I find written, that I know not the which to choose. Neither have I enough of leisure to take them all. Therefore will I do even as he does who seeks flowers in a meadow the which is all spring-like and bedecked with flowers, and who sees all around him so many divers ones, crimson, and violet, and yellow, and dark blue, that he knows not the which to pluck first. In like manner, I tell you, by the Holy Mother, I am much bewildered anent these old-time miracles of Our Lady, but since that you desire of me to rehearse yet more of them, that will I do. But this will I not do word for word, nor altogether in order, for never should I be ended."

GAUTIER DE COINCI.

# OF THE TUMBLER OF
# OUR LADY

# OF THE TUMBLER OF
## OUR LADY (1)

IN the " Lives of the Fathers," the matter of
which is of profit, a story is told, than which I
do not say that none more pleasing has been heard,
but this one is not so without worth, that it may
not well be told. Now will I tell and rehearse unto
you of that which happened to a minstrel.

So much had he journeyed to and fro in so many
places, and so prodigal had he been, that he became
a monk of a holy Order, for that he was weary
of the world. He wholly relinquished his horses,
and clothes, and money, and all that he had, and
then he withdrew him from the world, and never

3

more did he wish to return to it. Therefore he entered this holy profession, as has been said, at Clairvaux (2).

And when that this tumbler, who was so graceful, and fair, and comely, and well formed, became a monk, he knew not how to perform any office that fell to be done there. Of a truth, he had lived only to tumble, to turn somersaults, to spring, and to dance. To leap and to jump, this he knew, but naught else, and truly no other learning had he, neither the " Paternoster," nor the " Canticles," nor the " Credo," nor the " Ave Maria," nor aught that could make for his salvation.

And when that he had entered the Order, he saw men high shorn who communicated together by signs, and uttered not a word, and right surely he bethought him that in none other manner were they able to hold discourse. But soon were his doubts ended, for he learnt that speech forsooth was forbidden unto them for penance, wherefore at times

they were silent, and thus it likewise happened unto
him that ofttimes he himself had to keep silence.

And with such good grace, and for so long time,
did he remain silent, that never did he speak the
whole day long unless that command was given unto
him to speak, so that they oft made merry over it.
And he was sore affrighted in their midst, for he knew
not what to say, or what to do of all that fell to be
done there. And because of this, he was very sad
and pensive. And everywhere he saw the monks and
the novices each one serving God in such office as he
held. He saw the priests at the altars, for such was
their office, the deacons at the gospels, and the sub-
deacons at the epistles. And at the proper time, the
acolytes straightway rang the bell at the vigils. One
recited a verse, and another a lesson, and the young
priests were at the psalter, and the novices at the
misereres, and the least experienced were at the
paternosters, for in suchwise was their work ordered.
And he looked everywhere throughout the offices

and the cloisters, and saw hidden in the corners here four, here three, here two, here one. And he observed each one as closely as he was able. One made lamentation, another wept, and another groaned and sighed. And much did he marvel what ailed them. And at length he said, " Holy Mary, what ails these folk that they deport themselves thus, and make show in this manner of such grief ? Much disquieted must they be, it seems to me, when they all with one accord make such great dolour ! " And then he said, " Ah, miserable being ! By the Holy Mary, what have I said ? I trow that they pray God's grace. But, unhappy being that I am, what do I here, when that he who, in his calling, serves God with all his might, is thus enslaved ? Never shall I render any service here, for naught can I do or say. Very hapless was I when that I became a monk, for I know not how even to pray aright. I look hither and thither, and naught do I, save to waste time and to eat bread to no purpose. If in this

I am found out, I shall be utterly undone. I am a lusty villain, and if I do naught here but eat, I shall be turned out into the fields. Very miserable am I in this high office!"

Then he wept to allay his grief, and truly did he desire to be dead. "Holy Mother Mary," said he, "beseech your sovereign Father of His grace to guide me, and to bestow upon me such wisdom that I may be able to serve both Him and you in suchwise as to be worthy of the food which I eat here, for well know I that now I do wrong."

And when he had thus made lament, he went prying about the Church until that he entered a crypt, and he crouched down nigh unto an altar, and hid himself there as best he could. And above the altar was the image of Our Lady, the Holy Mary. And in nowise did it surprise him that he felt in safety there, and he perceived not that it was God, who well knows how to guide His own, who had led him there.

And when he had heard the bell ring for the Mass, he rushed forth from the crypt all trembling. "Ah!" said he, "I am like unto a traitor! Even now each one is saying his response, and here am I a tethered ox, and I do naught here but browse, and waste food in vain. Shall I therefore neither speak nor act? By the Mother of God, this will I do, and never shall I be blamed for it. I will do that which I have learnt, and thus, after mine own manner, will I serve the Mother of God in her Church. The others do service with song, and I will do service with tumbling."

And he took off his habit, and then stripped himself, and laid his garments beside the altar, but so that his body should not be uncovered, he kept on a tunic, the which was very clinging and close fitting. Little better was it than a shift; nevertheless was his body wholly covered. And thus was he fitly clad and equipped, and he girded his tunic, and duly prepared him, and he turned him to the image, and gazed on it very humbly. "Lady," said he, "to your keeping

I commend my body and my soul. Gentle Queen and Lady, despise not that which I am acquainted with, for, without ado, I will essay me to serve you in good faith, if so be that God will aid me. How to sing, or how to read to you, that I know not, but truly I would make choice for you of all my best tricks in great number. Now may I be like a kid which frisks and gambols before its mother. Lady, who art never stern to those who serve you aright, such as I am, I am yours."

Then he began to turn somersaults, now high, now low, first forwards, then backwards, and then he fell on his knees before the image, and bowed his head. "Ah, very gentle Queen!" said he, "of your pity, and of your generosity, despise not my service." Then he tumbled, and leaped, and turned gaily the somersault of Metz. And he bowed to the image, and worshipped it, for he paid homage to it as much as he was able. And anon he turned the French somersault, and then the somersault of Champagne, and after that, those of Spain and of Brittany, and then that of Lorraine. And he laboured to the utmost of his power.

And after that, he did the Roman somersault, and then he put his hand before his face, and turned him with great grace, and looked very humbly at the image of the Mother of God. "Lady," said he, "this is an honest performance. I do this not for mine own sake, so help me God, but for yours, and above all for the sake of your Son, and truly do I here declare unto you, that but little pleasure have I in it, save that I serve you, and thus acquit myself. The others serve, and I serve also. Do not despise your servant, for I serve you for your diversion. Lady, you are the *Monjoie* (3) which all the world proclaims."

Then he threw up his feet, so that no longer were they on the ground, and he went to and fro on his hands, and twirled his feet, and wept. "Lady," said he, "I do homage to you with my heart, and my body, and my feet, and my hands, for naught beside this do I understand. Now would I be your gleeman. Yonder they are singing, but I am come here to divert you. Lady, you who can protect me, for God's sake do not despise me." Then he beat his breast, and sighed, and mourned very grievously that he knew not how to do service in other manner. And then he turned a somersault backwards. "Lady," said he, " so help me God, never before have I done this. Lady! How that one would have his utmost desire, who could dwell with you in your right glorious mansion! For God's sake, Lady, receive me there. I do this for your sake, and in nowise for mine own." Then he again turned the somersault of Metz, and tumbled and capered full many a time.

And when he heard the monks celebrating, he began to exert himself, and so long as the Mass dured, he ceased not to dance, and to jump, and to leap, until that he was on the point to faint, and he could not stand up, and thus he fell to the ground, and dropped from sheer fatigue. And like as the grease issues from the spitted meat, so the sweat issued from him all over, from head to foot. "Lady," said he, "no more can I do now, but of a surety I shall come back again."

And he was quite overcome of heat. And he took up his clothing, and when that he was dressed, he took his leave, and he bowed to the image, and went his way. "Farewell, very gentle friend," said he. "For God's sake, grieve not at all, for if that I am able, and it is permitted unto me, I will come back, for each hour would I serve you to the utmost of my power, so gracious are you." And then he retired, gazing at the image. "Lady," said he, "what great pity is it that I know not all those psalters! Fain would I desire to know them for love of you, very gentle Lady. To you I commend my body and my soul."

And longwhiles he led this life, and, at each hour precisely, he repaired to the image, to render service and homage. Certes, so greatly did it please him,

and with such right good will did he do this, that
never a day was he so tired that he could not do his
very utmost to delight the Mother of God, and never
did he desire to do other service.

Well known was it that he went each day into the
crypt, but no one, save God, knew what he did there,
nor would he, for all the riches of the whole world,
that any, save the supreme God alone, should know
of his doings. Of a truth, fully did he believe that
whensoever this should become known, then would
he be driven out thence, and he would be sent back
to the world, the which was all overrun of sinners,
and rather would he be dead than ever again be the
companion of sinners. But God, who knew his purpose and his very great compunction, and the love
which moved him to it, would not that his deeds
should be hidden, but willed and suffered that the
service the which her lover had rendered to His
Mother, should be known and made manifest, to the
end that every one should know and understand and

perceive that God refuses no one who lovingly labours for Him, in whatsoever manner it may be, provided he loves God, and does right.

Think you now that God would have prized his service if that he had not loved Him ? By no means, however much he tumbled. But He prized it because of his love. Much labour and fatigue, many fasts and vigils, many tears and sighs and groans and prayers, much diligence in discipline, both at Mass and at matins, the bestowal of all that you have, and the payment of whatsoever you owe, if you love not God with all your heart, all these are wholly thrown away in such manner, understand well, that they avail naught for true salvation. Of a truth, without love and without pity, before God all counts for naught. God asks not for gold or for silver, but only for true love in the hearts of men, and this one loved God truly. And because of this, God prized his service.

Longwhiles did the good man live thus, but for

how long time he so lived contented, I cannot tell
unto you, but in the course of time sore trouble came
to him, for one of the monks, who in his heart greatly
blamed him that he came not to matins, kept watch
on him. And he much marvelled what happened,
and said that never would he desist until that he
knew who he was, and for what he was worth, and in
what manner he earned his bread. And so closely
did the monk pursue him, and follow him, and keep
watch on him, that he distinctly saw him perform
his service in a simple manner, even as I have told it
unto you. "By my faith," said he, " he has a good
time of it, and much greater diversion, it seemeth to
me, than we have all together. Whiles that the
others are at prayer, and at work in the house, this
one dances with as much vigour as if he had an
hundred silver marks (4). Right well does he perform
his service, and in this manner he pays for us that
which is his due. A goodly proceeding, this, forsooth ! We sing for him, and he tumbles for us !

We pay for him, and he pays for us! If we weep, he soothes us! I would that all the convent could see him at this very moment just as I do, even if I had to fast for it till dusk! Not one would there be, methinks, who would be able to restrain his laughter if that he witnessed the tumbling of this fellow, who thus kills himself, and who so excites him by tumbling, that he has no pity on himself. God counts it unto him for penance, for he does it without evil intent, and, certes, I hold it not to be ill, for, as I believe, he does it, according to his lights, in good faith, for he wishes not to be idle."

And the monk saw how that he laboured without ceasing all the day long. And he laughed much, and made merry over the matter, but it caused him sorrow as well as merriment. And he went to the abbot, and rehearsed unto him, from beginning to end, all that he had learnt, even as you have heard it.

And the abbot arose, and said to the monk, "On your vow of obedience, I command that you keep silence, and noise this not abroad, and that you so well observe this command, that you speak not of this matter save to me alone, and we will both go thither, and we shall see if this can be, and we will beseech the heavenly King, and His very gentle and dear Mother, who is so precious, and of so great renown, that she, of her sweetness, will go pray of her Son, her Father, and her Lord, that if it so pleases Him, He will this day suffer me to witness this service in such sort that God may be the more loved on account of this, and that, if thus it pleases Him, the good man may not be found worthy of blame for it."

And then they went thither quite quietly, and without delay they hid themselves in a covert nook nigh unto the altar, so that he saw them not. And the abbot, watching there, observed all the service of the novice, and the divers somersaults the which he turned, and how that he capered, and danced, and bowed before the image, and jumped, and leaped, until that he was nigh fainting. And so greatly was he overcome of fatigue, that he fell heavily to the ground, and so exhausted was he, that he sweated all over from his efforts, so that the sweat ran all down the middle of the crypt.  But in a little, the Mother of God, whom he served all without guile, came to his succour, and well knew she how to aid him.

And anon the abbot looked, and he saw descend from the vaulting so glorious a lady, that never had he seen one so fair or so richly crowned, and never had another so beautiful been created.  Her vesture was all wrought with gold and precious stones, and with her were the angels and the archangels from the heavens above, who came around the tumbler, and solaced and sustained him.  And when that they were ranged around him, he was wholly comforted, and they made ready to tend him, for they desired to make recompense unto him for the services the which he had rendered unto their Lady, who is so precious a gem.  And the sweet and noble Queen took a white cloth, and with it she very gently fanned her minstrel before the altar. And the noble and gracious Lady fanned his neck and body and face to cool him, and greatly did she concern herself to aid him, and gave herself up to the care of him ; but of this the good man took no heed, for he neither perceived, nor did he know, that he was in such fair company.

And the holy angels who remained with him, paid him much honour, but the Lady no longer sojourned there, and she made the sign of the cross as she turned away, and the holy angels, who greatly rejoiced to keep watch over their companion, took charge over him, and they did but await the hour when God would take him from this life, and they might bear away his soul.

And full four times did the abbot and the monk witness, without hindrance, how that each hour he went there, and how that the Mother of God came there to aid and succour her liegeman, for well knows she how to protect her own. And the abbot

had much joy of it, for very desirous had he been to
know the truth concerning it. Now had God verily
shown unto him that the services the which this poor
man rendered were pleasing unto Him. And the
monk was quite bewildered by it, and from anguish
he glowed like fire. " Your mercy, Sire ! " said he
to the abbot, " this is a holy man whom I see here.
If that I have said aught concerning him that is evil,
it is right that my body should make amends for it.
Therefore ordain me a penance, for without doubt
he is altogether an upright man. Verily have we
seen all, and no longer can we be mistaken."

And the abbot said, " You speak truly. God has
indeed made us to know that He loves him with a
very great love. And now I straightway give command unto you that, in virtue of obedience, and so
that you fall not under condemnation, you speak to no
one of that which you have seen, save to God or
to me."

" Sire," said he, " to this do I assent."

And at these words they departed, and no longer did they stay in the crypt, and the good man did not remain, but when that he had done all his service, he clothed himself again in his garments, and went to divert himself in the monastery.

And thus passed the time, until that, a little while after, it came to pass that the abbot sent for him who was so good. And when he heard that he was sent for, and that it was the abbot who made enquiry for him, so greatly was he troubled, that he knew not what he should say. "Alas," said he, " I am found out. Never a day passes without distress, or without toil or disgrace, for my service counts for naught. Methinks it is not pleasing unto God. Alas ! as the truth has been found out, I bethink me that it is displeasing unto Him. Can I conceive that these tricks, the which I do, could give pleasure to the Supreme God if that I did them openly ? No pleasure would they give Him. Alas ! I never do right. What shall I do, and what shall I say? Blessed and very dear God, what will become of me? Now shall I be rebuked and put to shame, and I shall be banished hence, and shall again become like unto a target for all the ill-treatment of the world without. Gentle Lady, Holy Mary, how troubled is my mind! I know not, Lady, from whom to get counsel, so come now to mine aid. Very dear God, help me now. Tarry not, but hasten, and bring with you your Mother. Of your mercy, come not without her, and do you both come to aid me, for verily I know not of myself how to plead my cause. And at the first word, anon will they say, Away with you! Woe is me! How shall I be able to make answer when I know not one single word with the which to make explanation? But what avails this? It behoves me to go."

And weeping, so that his face was all wet, he came before the abbot, and he knelt before him in tears.

"Sire," said he, "for God's sake, have mercy! Would you drive me hence? Tell me all your behests, and all your bidding will I do."

Then said the abbot, "This would I know, and I would that you answer me truly. Longwhiles have you been here, both winter and summer, and I would know by what services, and in what manner, you earn your bread."

"Alas," said he, "well knew I that all would become known, and that when all my doings were known, no longer would any one have to do with me. Sire," said he, "now will I depart hence. Miserable am I, and miserable shall I be, for I never do aught that is right."

Then the abbot made answer, "Never have I said this, but I pray and demand of you, and further I command you, that, in virtue of obedience, you wholly reveal unto me your thoughts, and tell unto me in what manner you serve us in our monastery."

"Sire," said he, "this will be my death! This command will kill me."

Then he straightway unfolded unto him, howsoever grievous it was, his whole life, from beginning to end, in such sort that he left naught unsaid, just as I have told it unto you. And with clasped hands, and weeping, he told and rehearsed unto him everything, and, sighing, he kissed his feet.

And the holy abbot turned to him, and, all weeping, raised him up. And he kissed both his eyes. "Brother," said he, "be silent now, for truly do I promise unto you that you shall be at peace with us. God grant that we may have your fellowship so long as we are deserving of it. Good friends shall we be. Fair, gentle brother, pray for me, and I will pray in return for you. And so I beseech and command of you, my sweet friend, that you forthwith render this service openly, just as you have done it, and still better even, if that you know how."

" Sire," said he, " are you in good earnest ? "

" Yea, truly," said the abbot, " and I charge you, on pain of penance, that you no longer doubt it."

Then was the good man so very joyous, so the story relates, that he scarce knew what he did. But despite himself, he was constrained to rest, for he had become all pale. And when that he was come to himself again, he was so overcome of joy, that he was seized with a sickness, of the which in a short space he died. But very cheerfully did he perform his service without ceasing, morning and evening, by night and by day, so that not an hour did he miss, until that he fell ill. Then verily such great sickness laid hold upon him, that he could not move from his bed. But that which distressed him the most, since never did he make complaint of his sufferings, was that he could not pay for his sustenance, for the which he was much troubled in mind, and moreover he feared that his penance would be in vain, for that he did not busy himself with such service as was his wont, and very deserving of blame did he seem unto himself to be.

And the good man, who was so filled with anguish, besought of God that He would receive him before that more shame came unto him. For so much grieved was he that his doings were become known, that he could not endure it. And he was constrained to lie down forthwith.

And greatly did the holy abbot hold him in honour, and he and his monks went each hour to chant beside his bed, and such great delight had he in that which was sung to him of God, that in nowise did he long for Poitou (5), so much did it pleasure him to learn that all would be pardoned unto him. And he made a good confession and repentance, but nevertheless he was fearful. And, as I have told unto you, at last it came to pass that he died.

And the abbot was there, and all his monks, and

the novices and good folk, who kept watch over him
very humbly, and quite clearly did they see a right
wondrous miracle. Of a truth they saw how that,
at his death, the angels, and the Mother of God,
and the archangels, were ranged around him. And
there, also, were the very evil and cruel and violent
devils, for to possess them of his soul, and no fancy
is this. But to no purpose had they so long lain
in wait for him, and striven so earnestly for him
and pursued him, for now no power had they over
his soul. And forthwith his soul quitted his body,
but in nowise was it lost, for the Mother of God
received it. And the holy angels who were there,
sang for joy, and then they departed, and bare it to
heaven, and this was seen of all the monks, and of all
the others who were there.

Now they wholly knew and perceived that God
willed it that the love of His good servant should no
longer be hid, and that all should know and perceive

his goodness, and they had great joy and great wonderment of it, and much honour did they pay to his body, and they carried it into the Church, and heartily did they celebrate the service of God. And they buried him with honour in the choir of the mother-church.

With great honour did they bury him, and then, like some saintly body, they kept watch over him. And anon, without concealing aught, the abbot told unto them all his doings, and his whole life, and all that he had seen in the crypt, even as you have heard it. And eagerly did the monks listen unto him. " Certes," said they, " well may it be believed. It cannot be misdoubted, for the truth bears witness to it. Fully is the matter proven, and certain is it that he has done his penance." And greatly did they rejoice together there.

Thus died the minstrel. Cheerfully did he tumble, and cheerfully did he serve, for the which he merited great honour, and none was there to compare unto him.

And the holy Fathers have related unto us that it thus befel this minstrel. Now let us pray God, without ceasing, that He may grant unto us so worthily to serve Him, that we may be deserving of His love. The story of the Tumbler is set forth.

Here endeth The Tumbler of Our Lady.

# NOTES

## THE TUMBLER

1. It seems probable that this story, here rendered from a thirteenth century MS., was founded upon one of Eastern origin introduced into France by the Crusaders, or was possibly one of many brought from India to Europe by the Arabs, the literary colporteurs of the Middle Ages. The main incident in it—the appearance of, and the solace given by, the Virgin, to a monk of Clairvaux—proclaims it as being told in honour of the Cistercian Order. A similar incident in honour of this Order is met with in another story, in which some young monks, suffering from the heat whilst reaping in a field at Clairvaux, are refreshed by the Virgin and her maidens, who come to them, and wipe the sweat from their brows. The French text of the present story suggests the end of the twelfth century as its date, and a native of Picardy, working in the Ile-de-France (perhaps at Paris), and possibly coming from one of the two celebrated centres of monastic learning—Corbie, near Amiens, or St. Riquier, near Abbeville—as the writer. These two monasteries owed their greatness principally to the dispersion, at the time of the Norman invasion, of the monks of the Abbey of St. Martin of Tours, who took refuge in Neustria, and particularly in the part now called Picardy. How deeply the East influenced

the West, and even the Church itself, may be gathered, amongst
other things, from such adaptations in literature as this story,
and also from illuminated MSS., in which, amongst other direct
borrowings, Salome may be seen represented upturned on her
hands, in Eastern fashion, before her father and his guests.   In a
seventh century Anglo-Saxon version of St. Mark's gospel, it is
said of Salome that " she jumped or leaped and pleased
Herod," and in one of the eleventh century, that " she tumbled
and it pleased Herod."   (On the subject of direct borrowings from
the East in early Christian art and literature, see Strzykowski's
*Orient oder Rom.*)

2. The monastery of Clairvaux (Clara Vallis, Bright Valley
of St. Bernard) was founded by St. Bernard A.D. 1114, and
was an offshoot of the great Abbey of the Cistercians at
Citeaux, in Burgundy.   The ruling principle of this reformed
congregation of the Benedictine Order was rigid self-abnega-
tion, whilst extreme simplicity was the characteristic of their
abbeys and monasteries.   Yet in spite of such austerity, this
branch of the Order was the most popular one, and extended
its influence far and wide.   The Order placed itself under the
especial protection of the Virgin, and, in her honour, adopted
a white habit, the colour consecrated to her purity.

3. By some, the Monjoie is said to have been a heap of
stones thrown together either in sign of victory, or of some
memorable event, or else to indicate the road.   The erection
of such heaps was the survival of a custom which existed
amongst many peoples in the remote past, and examples are
to be found in the New World as well as in the Old.   Sometimes they are found by the wayside where the road is dangerous
or difficult, and even to this day travellers, as they pass by in
safety, contribute their stone, by way, it would seem, of thank-

of.ering. In Greece, for instance, there was a Hermes Agyieus, *i.e.* protector of the roads, in whose honour, images (in the form of rough stones), or altars (often mere rough heaps of stones), were erected. The Romans, likewise, raised heaps of stones in honour of Mercury, who, like the Greek Hermes, was the patron of travellers in this world, as well as the conductor of souls to another (*cf.* Hermes Agetor). In the Middle Ages, the term Monjoie is also said to have been applied to the cross placed on the top of such heaps to point out the road to some holy place. There is, or was, an example of such a cross in the *Heures de Turin* (Plate 39), lately partially destroyed by fire, and which may still be seen in reproduction (V. & A. Mus.). The term was also used, in France, to designate the chief of the thirty heralds, who was called "Roi d'armes," and had the title "Monjoie St. Denis," and it may be recalled that in the play of Henry V., Shakespeare gives the name of Montjoy to the French herald. In the Middle Ages, Monjoie, or Monjoie St. Denis, also served as a battle-cry for the French, and was a term applied to the banner borne before the troops to guide the army. M. Marius Sepet, in his *Histoire du drapeau*, expresses the opinion that Monjoie was the name of a hill (now better known under the name of "Vatican"), on the N.W. of Rome, from which pilgrims first caught sight of the Basilica of the Holy Apostles, and, giving *Mons Gaudii* as the probable derivation of the word, considers it likely that this circumstance gave rise to the adoption of so characteristic a name. He adds that probably it was on this hill that Pope Leo III. gave to Charlemagne, in the presence of his army, the celebrated banner, a representation of which is to be found in St. John Lateran, and that, from the place where this happened, the name became associated with the banner itself, and Monjoie

became the French battle-cry. Later, when the standard of
St. Denis had become the chief banner, the ancient cry which
had been traditional since the time of Charlemagne was added
to the name of the saint, the two being united as "Monjoie-
Saint-Denis." Mont Jou, and Montjoie, are also the names of
many mountains and hillocks, natural and artificial. On the
Great St. Bernard Pass, near the Hospice, there was once a
temple to Jupiter Penninus. The mountain thence derived its
Italian name of Monte Jove, locally Monte Jou. It is possible
that the Montjoie St. Denis, near Paris, was originally a hill
dedicated to Jupiter, and that the Christian Saint took the place
of the Pagan God.

4. In the thirteenth century, the Silver Mark was worth forty
Parisian Sols, or two Parisian Pounds.

5. Possibly this is an allusion to the pilgrimage formerly
made to Poitiers by devotees who conveyed thither their sick
to be healed by the wonder-working body of St. Radegonde.
Although the body of the Saint was burnt during the religious
wars of the sixteenth century, the empty coffin is still supposed
to possess healing powers, and pilgrimages to it are still made.

OF A KNIGHT TO WHOM OUR
LADY APPEARED WHILST HE
PRAYED

*Of a Knight to whom Our Lady
appeared whilst he prayed.*

## OF A KNIGHT TO WHOM OUR LADY APPEARED WHILST HE PRAYED (1)

HE was a young Knight, I find, fair, pleasing, strong, and brave, of high degree, and of great renown. And his heart was set upon naught but jousts and tourneys (2) and combats in honour of a lady who had wholly made captive his heart. And he oft made large gifts and offerings of his goods, in order to win renown and praise. And whiles that he was yet young, it gave him joy at all times to do all her pleasure, even though it were irksome to him. And all this will I recount and tell to you. He was much feared, and of great authority, in his own land and in many places, and so exceeding hard to please was he, that he would not wed, for so distraught was his heart on account of this lady, that he never saw any woman whom he deemed worthy to take or to wed, nor was he known to grieve over this. But of such disposition was the lady, that naught would she have to do with him.

The knight, who was very handsome, had striven throughout the land in many combats and tournaments, and in many jousts and encounters, in her honour, and he wist not what more he could do. The lady was of such rank, of such beauty, and of such worth, that he would as lief have believed that he had stormed and taken Chalons (3) as that he could do aught pleasing unto her. And so very proudly did she bear herself toward him, that she did not show him due respect, even by making fair countenance. So proud did he find her, that never could he win from her, either by entreaty or by gifts, or by brave deeds of chivalry, solace either of love or of friendship. And the more he besought her, the

more did she harden herself, and the more he found
her cold, so much the more did he become fervent
and passionate.

And love made such sore pursuit of him, and so
assailed him in divers ways, that for a while he lost
all reason.

At length, when naught could conquer her, he
hied him to an abbot, a holy man, to discover unto
him the matter, and after a while the abbot said to
him that if he would trust in him, of a surety he
might know that he would have all his desire.

Then he made answer, " Good, kind sir, other
women have hearts of lead, but this one, I trow, has
a heart of iron.  Gladly would I that my soul should
burn in Hell, and little matters it to me what becomes
of me, so only that I win her love.  Sir, so much do
I love her, I tell you truly, that I can neither eat nor
drink nor sleep nor rest."

And the wise man ventured not to chide him, for
well knew he that, in such matters, the more men

are roused and excited, by so much the more is hurt and ill done to them. He well knew and perceived that in no way could he give counsel in this affair unless God and His Mother lent him their aid.

"Brother," said he, "if you but trust me, and cease not to do that which I pray of you, know that in this matter you shall be as well counselled as you can best desire."

"All your pleasure, sir, will I do, and on my oath I will be your man, if so be I can prevail at last. Naught is there in the world so grievous to do, that would not be easy to me in order to achieve so great a thing."

"Fear not, Brother," said he, "that it will trouble you too sorely to do that which I tell you. Every day, for a year, you must repeat to me an hundred and fifty times (4), on your bended knees, the sweet Ave of the Mother of God."

"Gladly even two thousand times if you will," said he, "for so mad am I for her love, that I care not what I do, if but I win her love and her favour."

Then said the holy man, " Fair sweet friend, in many more weighty matters has the Mother of God given counsel, but by reason of the life you lead, greatly do I fear me that you may be forgetful. Since you are a young Esquire, so much do you love deeds of chivalry, and fishing and the chase, that I fear me, and have great doubt, that you will fail me in your covenant."

" Sir," said he, " you mock me. By St. John, to achieve so great a thing, rather would I be a monk, shaven and shorn, in your cloister, for a whole year, than make default for a single day, or do any misdeed. My heart neither sleeps nor rests, so much has her love laid hold on me and bound me."

Thereupon the holy man embraced him, and smiling, said to him, " Fair Brother, if God wills to heal you of this ill, through the mediation of His Mother you can end it "

Then the knight departed, and no longer did he
venture to roam abroad. Truly did he keep well
his covenant with Our Lady and the wise man. He
neither tourneyed nor jousted, but dwelt in his
chapel more than in any other place. Then happened
an adventure, the which fell out for him better than
he thought for. To much trouble and care did he
put himself to salute Our Lady. Scarce would he
stir, day or night, from his chapel, and oft did he call
on the Mother of God, and earnestly beseech of her
to give him joy of his Love, who was so fair that it
seemed to him that she was like unto the moon in the
heavens. And when that he saw the end of the year
drawing nigh, he thought quite soon to have his wish
to see his Love, and his heart and his soul were so
stirred and so blithe, so gay and so full of joy, that
he sang and descanted new songs and ditties night
and day. And for that he wearied of the sojourn
which had dured well-nigh a year, early on a morn
in summer he went to hunt in a forest for to divert

and to solace him. And in the forest, as if God willed it, he lost his men, nor knew he which way the hunt had turned. And whiles that he sought it, and followed the track, he happened on an old chapel, much ruined and laid waste. " Ah, Mother of God, have mercy on me! Longwhiles is it since I was here! " said he. " Noble Lady, noble maid, within this old chapel will I pay you that which I owe you." Then straightway he alighted, and entered the little chapel, and on his bare knees he said one hundred and fifty Aves before the little old image of Our Lady. " Ah, noble maid ! " said he, " accomplish for me now my great desire for my Love who is so fair, for naught is there in the world that I so greatly long for. So beautiful is she, that it seemeth to me that never was there formed by Nature a creature so fair in body, and arm, and hand, and face, and all my heart is set on her. Alas! if in this I do not have my desire, of a surety my soul will quit my body."

In such manner did he make complaint unto himself before the image of Our Lady, and much he made lament, and much did he grieve, and he heaved many deep sighs. And of a sudden the Mother of God, who by her great tenderness and gracious courtesy has delivered many a sufferer from his durance, showed herself to the unhappy one who so sorely called upon her and besought her, crowned with a crown full of precious stones, so sparkling and so glorious, that for a while his eyes were dazzled by them. Moreover they glistened and shimmered like unto the rays which shine on a summer's morn. And so beautiful and bright was her countenance, that happy did that one seem to himself to be who could look longwhiles upon it.

" Fair friend," said Our Lady, " is she who is the cause of your sighs, and has so disquieted you, fairer than I ? "

And so sore afraid was the knight at the brightness, that he knew not what to do, and he covered his face with his hands, and such dismay and awe possessed him, that he fell to the ground with fear. But she who is all-pitiful said to him, " Friend, be not afraid. I am she, doubt it not, who must win you your Love. Take heed what you do now, so that you may have for Love the one of us whom you love best."

" Lady," said he, " no longer do I desire her, if that I can have you in her stead, for I know of a truth that you are worth nigh a thousand and fifty of her, and well may she be gone if that I can have such exchange for her."

" Fair friend," said Our Lady, " if I find you a loyal lover, there above, in Paradise, will you find me a loyal friend, and through me and my love will you find more of joy and solace and fellowship than you can conceive. But it is meet, doubt it not, that for a year you do for me as much as you have done for your other Love. Never for my sake strive in any tourney or other deeds of chivalry, but if that you would be lord of my love, repeat an hundred and fifty Aves for a year without missing a day. Then will you win me without doubt, and thus will you hold and possess my whole love for ever and ever."

And thereupon she departed from him, and the knight tarried not, but went to seek the good abbot, and, weeping, he told and discovered unto him that which he had erewhiles heard. And at this the holy man was much o'erjoyed, and fervently did he give thanks to the Mother of the God who has created all. And at length, by the counsel of the wise man, the knight became a monk, and yet the more to withdraw himself from the world, he cut his hair unevenly, and shaved his head, the which was fair and smooth, and he withdrew himself from his Love, and in suchwise he gave himself to Our Lady. With all his heart, and with all his soul, did he love her, and he had her in such remembrance, that he could neither eat nor drink, and he sighed deeply, and ever bare in his heart the remembrance of her great beauty.

And at the end of the year, the Mother of God, without tarrying, came back to seek him, for no longer would she leave him upon earth, but, like a true friend, she took him to eternal life on high, there where all her friends have endless joy and solace of her love.

Here is unfolded the Miracle of the Knight to whom
Our Lady appeared.

# NOTES

## KNIGHT AND LADY

1. M. Mussafia places this miracle amongst a group which he calls that of the " Virgin's bridegrooms." In this instance, the Virgin, in being represented as combating with an earthly rival for the love of a man, is assigned a singularly human attitude. The story is said to be concerned with an English knight, who, in sore mental anguish, consulted a Cistercian Abbot, and to have been introduced into France by Eustace II., Abbot of St. Germer of Flaix, in the diocese of Beauvais, on his return from a mission to England, whither he went in 1200-1.

2. The Joust and the Tourney were two of the military exercises in use in the Middle Ages. The Joust was a combat between horsemen single-handed, and the Tourney one in which several were engaged on each side. In both, the lance was the weapon generally used, and from a proclamation made in the reign of Henry VII., it appears that the reward in each case differed. Military games, whose principal object it was to keep the soldier, in times of peace, ever prepared for war, had long been known. They were practised in classic times, and were engaged in by the ancient Germans. But the grand spectacle of a tournament is not found referred to, in French MSS., before

the eleventh century, and it was not till the early part of the twelfth century that it was introduced into England. It seems to owe its origin to the French, but several nations claim its invention, and it is very doubtful when and where tournaments, in the proper sense of the term, were first instituted. Perhaps the most picturesque modern account of a tournament is the one to be found in Sir Walter Scott's " Ivanhoe."

3. Perhaps this alludes to the hard-won victory of the allied Franks and Visigoths over Attila and his Huns, in the fifth century, in the neighbourhood of Chalons. This was so signal an overthrow of the barbarian host which swept like a scourge over Europe, that it has been counted by Sir E. Creasy among the " Fifteen decisive Battles of the World." Evidently the taking of Chalons was looked upon as an almost impossible feat.

4. One hundred and fifty formed the number of the *small* beads of the complete rosary, this representing the number of Ave-Marias to be recited as intercessions to the Virgin. Fifteen *large* beads were added to serve for the Pater Nosters. The use of the chaplet of beads for personal devotions was of Eastern origin, but its development into the Rosary was the invention of St. Dominic, in the beginning of the thirteenth century. Pictorial representations of this invention poetically show St. Dominic kneeling in front of an altar, and receiving the Rosary as a gift from the Virgin.

OF THE KNIGHT WHOSE PLACE
AT THE TOURNAMENT WAS
TAKEN BY OUR LADY

## OF THE KNIGHT WHOSE PLACE AT THE TOURNAMENT WAS TAKEN BY OUR LADY (1)

HOLY Jesus, how well does that one fight, and how nobly does he tourney, who of his own free will betakes him to the church where the holy service is being said, and where the holy mystery of the sweet Son of the Virgin Mother is being celebrated. As an ensample of this, I will rehearse a story even as I find it.

A cèrtain knight, who was courteous and wise, bold and of great prowess, than whom there was none better in chivalry, greatly loved the Virgin Mary. And to make show of his followers, and to make trial of his free men-at-arms, he set out for a tournament,

surrounded by his retainers. And thus it pleased
God that when the day of the tournament was come,
he made haste to be mounted, for much did he
desire to be first in the field. And he heard the bells
of a church which was nigh, the which were being
sounded for the celebration of the Holy Mass. And
without demur, the knight repaired straight to
the church to hearken to the service of God, and
anon a Mass of the holy Virgin Mary was chanted
heartily and devoutly, and then another was begun,
and the knight listened to it with attention, and
prayed fervently to Our Lady. And when that the
Mass was ended, the tierce was forthwith begun in
the same place.

"Sire," said his esquire unto him, "by the holy
body of God, the hour of the tournament passes.
Why do you remain here? Come away, I pray of
you. Would you become a hermit, or a dissembler,
or a hypocrite? Let us away to our task."

"Friend," said the knight, "most worthily does

he tourney who pays heed to the service of God, and when that the Masses are quite ended, we will go on our way. Before that, so please God, I will not go, but then, by the will of God, I will go tourney boldly." And after this, he held his peace.

And he turned his face to the altar, and remained in holy orisons until that the chanting was quite ended. Then they mounted, as it behoved them to do, and they rode towards the place where the games were to be held. And the knights who had been utterly vanquished, and were returning from the tournament, met him who had won all the prizes. And these who were on their way back, saluted and gave hearty welcome to the knight who was on his way from the Masses the which he had heard, and they said that of a truth never before had any knight done such feats of arms as he had done that day, for the which he would for all time be had in honour. And many were there who yielded them prisoners to him, and said, " Your prisoners are we, nor can we deny that you have overcome us in arms."

Then no longer was he astonished, for he straightway perceived that she, for whose sake he had been in the chapel, had appeared for him in the combat.

And without ado, he called together his barons, and said to them, " Of your charity, listen to me now, all of you, for of such a marvel will I tell you, that the like you have never heard before."

Then he recounted unto them, word for word, how that he had listened to the Masses, and how that he had not been present at the tournament, and had borne neither lance nor sword, but verily did he believe that the Maiden, to whom he had prayed in the chapel, had done battle for him. " A right glorious tournament has this been in the which she has contended for me, but to too base an end will she have striven if that I do not do battle for her, and foolish shall I be if that I return to the vanities of the world. Truly do I make promise unto God

that never again will I tourney save before the true
Judge, who knows the good knight, and judges him
according to his deeds."

Then he took his leave of them sorrowfully, and
tenderly did they weep much at this. And he departed from them, and thenceforth, in an abbey, he
served the Virgin Mary, and let us well believe that
he kept in the way that leads to a good end.

From this example, well do we perceive that the
good God in whom we put our trust, loves and
cherishes and honours him who, of his own free will,
tarries to hear Mass in the holy church, and does
service to his very gentle and dear Mother. Profit-
able is this habit, and he who is courteous and wise,
willingly maintains the good custom the which he
has learned in his youth, and desires to keep to it
all his life.

# NOTE

## OF THE KNIGHT AND THE TOURNAMENT

1. This story of the Virgin acting the part of a knight is taken from the "Golden Legend" of Jacobus de Voragine, a Dominican compiler of saintly legends, who lived in the thirteenth century. A like miracle is recorded of various knights, congratulated for prowess displayed in tournaments in which they never engaged.

# OF THE CLERK AND THE RING

*Of a Clerk who put a ring
on the Image of Our Lady.*

## OF THE CLERK AND
## THE RING (1)

**K**EEP silence, good folk, and I will recite unto you a miracle of much avail to arouse wrong doers to fulfil that which they have made promise of unto God. Much ill do all those expose themselves to, and thus do themselves hurt, who in aught fail in that of which they make promise unto God and His very gentle Mother.

My book, and the matter of it, relate how that the people had set up an image in front of an old church, for that they were restoring the church. And they laid their alms at the foot of the image as they passed before it. And oft did the young folk gather together there to play at ball, and to run races.

And on a day, many young clerks were playing at
ball before the portal of the church where this image
was set up.  And one of the clerks, who had on his
hand a ring the which his Love had given him,
played with much skill.  But love had made him
very fearful, and he would not for much that the
ring of his Love should be either lost or broken.
And he went towards the church for to put the
ring down in some place the while he joined in the
game.  And whilst he pondered in his heart, he
looked around him, and he saw the image the which
was lately new.  And when he saw that it was so
beautiful, he kneeled before it devoutly with tearful
eyes, and he bowed before it, and saluted it.  And
in a little while, the desire of his heart was changed.
" Lady," said he, " henceforth will I serve you all my
life long, for never shall I look upon any lady, or
damsel, or maiden, so pleasing and so fair.  A hundred
thousand (2) times fairer and more pleasing are you
than she who has given me this ring.  To her had I

surrendered my every wish, and my whole heart, but for the sake of you I would fain cast her aside, and her love and her jewel. This ring, the which is very beautiful, would I give you out of true love, in token that never will I have lover or wife, save you alone, fair sweet Lady."

And forthwith he placed the ring which he held, on the finger of the image, the which was quite straight. Then suddenly the image bent its finger so firmly, that no one could remove the ring if he would not destroy it.

Then was the youth sore dismayed, and he cried out aloud from fear. And no one was there, old or young, in the large square, who hastened not to him, and he told unto them of all that he had said and done to the image. Then each one crossed himself, and marvelled at it, and each one counselled him that not a day should he make delay, but that he should abandon the world, and become a monk, and all his days serve God and the Holy Mary, who well showed unto him, by her finger, that dearly should he love her, and that none other lover could he have. But he had not enough of discretion to keep his covenant. Rather did he so put it out of remembrance, that seldom or never did he think on it.

And day by day the passion of the clerk for his Love grew and increased, and it so blinded him, that he saw naught beside. Wholly did he forget the Mother of God, and very foolish was he that he did not put his trust in her, and withdraw himself from the love of her to whom the ring had belonged. So set was his heart upon her, that he forsook Our Lady, and wedded her, and took her to wife. And they were richly wedded, for he had great wealth, and was of noble birth and proud lineage.

Then forthwith the gentle, gracious Lady, who is sweeter than honey in the honey-comb, appeared unto him. And it seemed to the clerk that Our Lady showed the finger with the ring, the which marvellously well fitted it, for that the finger was smooth and straight. " In nowise," said she, " have you done aright or loyally by me. Very basely have you behaved to me. Behold the ring of your mistress, the which you gave me in true love. Moreover, you said that an hundred times fairer and more pleasing was I than you had weened. A loyal friend would you have had in me if that you had not forsaken me. You give up the rose for the nettle, and the sweet-briar for the elder-bush. So deceived are you by love, that you give up the fruit for the leaf, the sea-lamprey for the river-lamprey (3), and the honey-comb and the sweet honey for poison and for gall."

And the clerk, who much marvelled at the vision, awoke. And he was sore affrighted, and thought to find the image by his side, and he felt all about him with his hands, but naught could he find there. Then he thought himself to be deceived, but he knew not what to think, and anon he fell asleep once more.

And forthwith the Mother of God appeared unto him again in anger. And she regarded him with a frowning countenance, terrible, wrathful, and scornful, and verily it seemed to the clerk, and he bethought him, that he was not worthy to look upon her, for she made semblance that she hated him, and she chided and menaced him, and heaped shame and insult upon him, and full many a time did she call him false and a perjurer, and a traitor and a renegade. "You are, forsooth, an abandoned and blinded caitiff," said Our Lady, "in that you have renounced and forsaken me for your sorry wife."

And the clerk sprang up all trembling, for well might it be that he was lost and ruined, since he had angered Our Lady.

Then said the clerk, all weeping, "Counsel me, Holy Spirit, for I perceive that if I remain longer here, anon shall I be altogether undone." And he sprang up from his bed, and no longer made delay, for to this was he inspired by the gracious Lady, who never did harm to man or woman.

Therefore he fled to a hermitage, and became a monk. And there he served God and the Holy Mary all his days. And he desired to dwell evermore in the retreat with his Lover upon whose finger, as a true friend, he had put the ring for love.

# NOTES

## OF THE CLERK AND THE RING

1. The earliest form of this story would seem to occur in the *Gesta Regum* of William of Malmesbury, written about A.D. 1125, which tells of an adventure that happened to a young man at Rome, who put a ring on the finger of a statue of Venus. In the form in which a ring is given to an image of the Virgin, the story also occurs in the *Speculum Historiale* of Vincent de Beauvais, who died A.D. 1264.

2. This is an Arabic form of the superlative which frequently occurs in mediæval stories, showing Eastern influence. Arabic elements filtered into France through Spain, as well as coming direct from the East.

3. In old French, the word here rendered "river-lamprey," is "Setueille" (sept-œil), from seven small marks on the head. It seems to have been the common name for a small lamprey, but it is uncertain whether it here means a *young sea*-lamprey, or a *river*-lamprey, as either epithet might be considered derogatory when used by way of comparison.

# OF THE MONK AND THE
## FIVE ROSES

*Of five roses that were found*
*in a monk's mouth after his death.*

# OF THE MONK AND THE
## FIVE ROSES (1)

I WILL recount unto you a short and very seemly
miracle of a simple monk. Simple was he, and
simply and devotedly he served God faithfully. He
was not such a clerk as the holy St. Anselm, but in
right good faith he repeated the miserere and the
seven psalms, and that which he had learned in
childhood, and with simple-hearted purpose, and
great devotion, did he serve the Mother of God,
whom he loved dearly. Ofttimes did he, all in
tears, invoke her on his bare knees. But he was
much harassed in mind, and troubled in great
measure, for that he knew not a fitting prayer by

the which he might hold him in due remembrance of the right glorious Lady.

And so much did he ponder this in his mind, that at last he bethought him of one in accordance with his understanding.  For his meditation, he took five psalms from the five letters of Maria.  And he duly bethought him that he might employ a psalm for each letter.  And none other philosophy or token did he seek of the Virgin Mary, whom he much loved, and held dear.

And ofttimes did he repeat the prayer.  And these are the names of the five psalms, the " Magnificat," the " Ad Dominum," and the " Retribue servo tuo."  And the fourth was the " In convertendo," and the " Ad te levavi " was the fifth.  And in honour of the sweet and most holy name, he rehearsed this holy psalmody as long as his life dured.  And when it pleased God that his end should come, there happened a very beauteous

miracle, for, held fast in his mouth, were found
five fresh roses, bright, crimson, and leafy, as if
newly gathered.

(2) Right well does this miracle make manifest to us
how loving and gracious is the sweet Mother of the
King of Glory, whom each day he had in remembrance. In nowise could he be discomforted, and
of this every one should be assured.

This miracle should show us that we should hasten,
with fear and trembling, to serve her, for she made
manifest that she held these five psalms, the which
I have cited, in great esteem. These five roses
should signify to all who read herein, that once each
day, at the least, they should repeat them on their
knees, with folded hands, before the image of the
Maiden who suckled and nourished her Son and
her Father.

Well does God serve those who serve His Mother.
And her love can no one deserve except by serving

her honestly. Goodly deserts, and joy without end, do all those deserve who serve her. Thus should each one of us serve her as much as her sweet love deserves.

# NOTES

## MONK AND FIVE ROSES

1. There are many variants of this story, sometimes roses, sometimes lilies, being found in the mouth of the holy dead. The idea of the five psalms and the five roses is said to have come from the East, for it is recorded how that, upon an Archbishop, when staying at the abbey of St. Bertin, at St. Omer, on his way home from Rome, relating that it was the custom, in the Holy Land, to say daily five psalms whose initials formed the word " Maria," one of his hearers observed the custom for the rest of his life, and at his death five roses were found issuing from his mouth, one of them having on it the word " Maria." This is evidently a monkish story invented to account for the fact that Eastern customs, somewhat transformed, were gradually penetrating the West.

2. This ending to the miracle is not to be found in the original text, and must have been added somewhat later by a copyist. It is retained here as an example of the way in which these stories were adapted to the practical ends of the Church's teaching. As a slight relief from what must have been boredom even to a saintly soul, the last few lines, in moralisings of this sort, were generally made to turn upon the frequent reiteration of two or more words composed of, or ending in, the same syllable.

OF THE HOLY SHIFT OF
CHARTRES

# OF THE HOLY SHIFT OF
## CHARTRES

THE story here set out tells how, by means of the Holy Shift the which is enshrined at Chartres, there befell, in the year of the Incarnation, 900, a wondrous miracle, of the which I will make mention.

For nigh eight years, so the record tells, one Charles (1), who was the son of the King Louis who had for surname " the Stammerer," had been king of France, and of the country around (2). And it came to pass that in the time of this King Charles, there came into France, the which was then much disturbed, a tyrant called Rollo (3), who at that time was also called Raoul. And this tyrant led a large army into France, for that he would fain succour the Pagans and the

Saracens beyond the sea, who were all despoiled.
And he laid waste France and the country around, and
slew and put to the sword all who could in nowise
withstand him, and never did he stay him until that
he was come to Etampes the Royal, where he repaired
many great flails (4).  And from thence he departed
to Chartres, and laid siege to it on every side.

And the Pagans laid siege to Chartres.  And the
citizens within, who were assailed, were affrighted,
for that they received great hurt from the mangonels
and the perriers (5), the which hurled stones at their
walls both in front and in their rear.

And when they saw the stones falling, and they
were not able to find shelter from them, or to
sally forth or to fight, and saw those without who
laboured and toiled to demolish the walls and assailed
them with great vigour, they held themselves to be
in jeopardy.  Thus were they in sore dismay, and no
trust had they in any help, save in the succour of the
maiden who is called the Lady of Chartres.  And

they besought aid of her who held sovereignty over Chartres.

Then they took the holy shift of the Mother, the which aforetime was prized in Constantinople, and of which a great king of France, Charles (6), who from childhood was called " the Bald," made a precious and noble gift to Chartres.   This king gave it to Chartres, for the which he thought to have recompense of the Lady who wore it when she bare within her the Son of God, since she would that it should be put in her chief church at Chartres, and that it should be alway guarded in that place, of the which she was called Lady.

And the Chartrains carried the holy vestment round the walls, and set it up on the battlements in place of an ensign and a banner.   And when their enemies saw it, they held it in great disdain, and mocked and laughed amongst themselves.   And they cast quarrels (7), and arrows, and Turkish darts (8), and bolts at it.   But God, who took heed of their unbelief, displayed His divine vengeance there, and so struck them with blindness, that they lost their sight, and could no longer see, and thus they could not retreat, neither could they go forward.

And when that the Chartrains beheld the miracle, and saw that which the Lady of Chartres had done for them, then were they filled with joy, and they prepared them to sally forth, and they armed them, and put on their hauberks, and made fast their helms, and with their Bishop Gasselin, who, for their defence and protection, bare the holy shift, the which is also called the veil of the Virgin, they all sallied forth from Chartres in great force, and with much clamour.   And they all threw themselves upon the host of the Pagans, so that great slaughter ensued, and it befell them according to their desire.

And of the slain there was such plenty, that the ground was strewn with them, and so many were

slain, that the swords of the Chartrains were soaked
in the blood of the heathen.   And as they scoured
the country, there met them, with a great company,
Richard, Duke of Burgundy, who led the bold comrades who were with him.   And the Frankish host,
the which had wrought such sore slaughter in the
flight, was now doubled.   And the Chartrains, the
Franks, and the Burgundians struck lustily with lance
and sword, and all banded them together to smite the
mischievous infidel folk.

And when Rollo saw that the strength of his
enemies was thus increased, and that his men were
cut to pieces, and that none were able to avenge
themselves, he forthwith took to flight.   So he fled
with a few men, and with but ten knights of the
many horsemen with the which he had set out, he
retreated to Lisieux.   And of his host, one part, the
which the Christians pursued, was quickly put to
flight.   And those who were without a leader, with-

drew them to the top of a hill, and there for one day did they defend themselves, when at last there came of a sudden to the assault the Count of Poitiers, with a great company of knights, and he saw the heathen on the hill, and encompassed them about on every side. But these, who knew many a ruse, made their escape in the middle of the night, and passed through the Frankish host.

And when that day was come, and the Franks saw that the heathen were escaped, they sprang on to their horses, and pursued them. And the horses were fresh and fleet, and at last they were come up with them. But the heathen strewed the way with the dead beasts, all blood-stained, the which were lying around, and thus in nowise could they do them any hurt. And the Franks, who longwhiles had given chase, turned back. And each one took off his helm, and they repaired them to their tents, and the heathen, like sorrowing folk, escaped

straightway from death by the sword to their Lord
at Lisieux.

Thus did Mary, the Lady of Chartres, succour the
Chartrains by means of her glorious shift. And her
veil, of the which I have spoken, should be very
lovingly regarded as of proven virtue.

# NOTES

## CHARTRES

1. Charles III. (the Simple), was the son of Louis II. (the Stammerer), and the great-grandson of Charlemagne. He was a mere puppet king, and during his reign Brittany, and the Lower Seine (afterwards called Normandy), were ceded to the Northmen.

2. The kingdom of France may be said to date from the Treaty of Verdun, A.D. 843, which fixed the Scheldt, the Meuse, and the Rhone as its boundaries. By the end of the ninth century, the portion included between the Seine and the Meuse, with Paris as its principal town, became the king's domain proper. The remainder, though under the suzerainty of the king, was divided into duchies and counties, and counties within the duchies, ever at war with each other, and each with its own laws and language.

3. This Rollo afterwards became the first Duke of Normandy, and was an ancestor of William the Conqueror. When Charles III., yielding to necessity, made peace with him, he gave him his daughter in marriage, and also ceded to him Normandy, and Brittany if he could conquer it.

4. A flail was a military weapon resembling a threshing flail in construction, but usually of iron, or strengthened with iron,

and often having the striking part armed with spikes. (Murray's
"New English Dictionary.") It is referred to in Spenser's
"Faerie Queene," V. ix. 19), where we read,

> "But when he would to a snake againe
>  Have turned himself, he with his yron flayle
>  Gan drive at him with so huge might and maine,
>  That all his bones as small as sandy grayle
>  He broke."

An example of the flail may be seen on the portal of the
Cathedral of Verona (twelfth century) in the hand of Roland,
one of the paladins of Charlemagne, who is generally represented
with the "olifant" (an ivory horn), whilst his companion, Oliver,
holds the traditional sword.

5. The mangona and mangonel, both included in the term
"perrier," were fixed engines for hurling stones, the former for
casting large stones, and the latter smaller ones. They were
generally employed in battering walls, but were sometimes used
for encountering an approaching enemy. They consisted of a
beam, with a sling fixed at one end of it from which a stone
was projected, the beam being raised or lowered by means of a
counterpoise at the other end. Sometimes ropes were also
attached in order to move the beam. The perrier proper
differed from the mangonel, inasmuch as it was movable,
being on wheels. It was principally made of wood. Both the
mangonel and the perrier were a kind of balista, an engine of
classic times, used for casting darts, fire-brands, and stones.
(Hewitt, "Ancient Armour and Weapons in Europe.") The
mangona is mentioned in the ninth century by Abbo, a monk
of St. Germain-des-Prés, in his description of the siege of Paris

(A.D. 886), and is pictorially represented as early as the thirteenth century.

6. Son of Louis le Debonnaire, and grandson of Charlemagne. He bestowed on the Cathedral of Chartres the holy shift, or veil as it is sometimes called, of the Virgin, which may still be seen by the faithful. It is said to have been given by the Empress Irene to Charlemagne at Constantinople. This Charles, in spite of troubles arising from constant petty warfare, was a great patron of learning, and much encouraged the school of Tours, founded, during the reign of his grandfather, Charlemagne, by Alcuin of York, afterwards Abbot of Tours, and from whence issued, for a time, the earliest complete texts of the Bible. He also invited to France Johannes Scotus (Erigena), a great scholar, and perhaps the last representative of Greek philosophy, and the first of the philosophy of the Middle Ages, and made him the head of his Palace School. Charles's reign also saw the dawn of the first European *mental* effort—Scholasticism—which was ultimately to be so disintegrated by the expansion of thought which was the outcome of the Crusades—the first European *popular* effort.

7. The name of quarrel, or bolt, was given to the missiles discharged from the cross-bow, or arbalest, because of the four-sided form of its head. Quarrels were of two kinds, one feathered, the other ending in a rough knob. They were carried after the army in carts, fifty being the provision for each cross-bow. The cross-bow appears to have been first recognised as a military weapon towards the close of the twelfth century.

8. It seems impossible to determine exactly what Turkish darts were, but it is possible that they were darts or arrows smeared with saltpetre and other combustible materials, as the employment of projectiles with burning mixtures was known in

the East of Europe as early as the seventh century. It would seem that their use in Western warfare was due to the Arabs, and we learn from an Arabic treatise, that they had made quite a science of the manufacture and employment of incendiary missiles, the elements of which knowledge they had, in all probability, received from the Chinese, as certain expressions, such as "Chinese arrows," used by them at an early period for these diabolical missiles, would seem to attest.

# OF THE DROWNING MAN
## DELIVERED

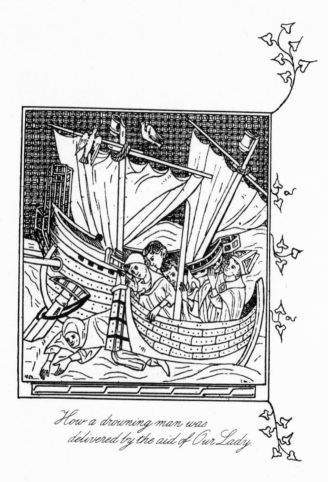

*How a drowning man was
delivered by the aid of Our Lady.*

# OF THE DROWNING MAN
## DELIVERED

WHOSO would hear and understand in what manner the Mother of God knows how to save from harm all who love her when they pray to her and entreat her, if that his interest moves him to this, let him hearken unto me, and a marvellous thing will he come to know.

It happened on a time, as I have read, that some clerks and lay folk crossed over the sea in a ship, to go to the Holy Sepulchre. But ere they were midway, a very violent and grievous storm struck their ship on all sides, the which did such damage to it on one side, that the master saw that of a surety in a short space all would be wrecked, and that each one must needs save himself as best he could. And

when that the master of the ship saw that immediate
death awaited them, he, and likewise a Bishop and
those of highest degree who were there, entered
straightway into a boat which they had, but one
among them, who thought to leap from the ship into
the boat, fell into the sea, and the sea swallowed him
up, and he was all engulfed, and no more was he
seen, into so deep an abyss was he fallen.

And of those who were in the boat, there were perchance forty in all.   Then in nowise could the master
keep silence, but weeping, he cried out aloud, " Sirs,
Sirs, naught is there left to be done but to lift on
high your hearts and your hands, and thus let each
one make supplication for his soul, and call on God
and Our Lady, and forthwith make confession,
for know of a surety that no longer is there any
chance for your lives, for the ship is sinking and is
lost."

Then there arose a great cry, and many tears were
shed.   And they all strove one with the other who

could make best confession, for they saw death before
them. And the boat had not gone far when the ship,
on the which were many folk, foundered, and was
lost. And the Bishop, who was a very good and
kindly man, and all his other companions, much
bewailed their comrades whom they saw thus in
distress. And they all fervently besought the
gracious and gentle Jesus Christ that He would have
mercy on those who were repairing to His sepulchre,
and were drowned. And the good Bishop took good
heed, and looked steadfastly down into the sea, to
learn if he could discover aught of the shipwrecked
ones down below.

And whilst that he thus looked around him, above
and below, before and behind, by the grace of the
Holy Spirit he saw white doves (1) to come forth from
the sea and straightway fly to Paradise, now two,
now three, now five, now ten. And the Bishop knew
of a truth that the white doves, the which flew to
heaven, were the souls of the good pilgrims whom the

just and perfect God, who all His own find just, had taken straight to heaven. Then was his grief re-doubled, and he exclaimed, " Ah ! Jesus Christ, my God, my God, my dear God, I doubt me if ever, all my life long, I have rendered one single service the which has been pleasing unto you. But never has your love been lacking, and a right good thing would it have been if that I had been shipwrecked together with my other companions. Rather would I be a dove, and soar in safety to the stars, than be an Archbishop or a Bishop. Foolish is he who craves for honour in this life, where all is changeful to the un-doing of folk, and very fleeting. But he who wings his flight on high, will evermore be in safety."

Thus did the Bishop make great dole and lamen-tation for a whole fortnight. And when it pleased God that they should reach land, they scanned the shore. And they saw their comrade come forth from the sea on to the beach, all unharmed. And they saw him who had fallen backwards into the sea

when that he would have leaped into the boat, thus
escaped from mishap. And it was not meet that
joy thereat should be lacking, and be well assured that
it was not. And so much did they kiss and embrace
him on the beach, that they did him some hurt. And
above all did the Bishop give him hearty welcome.
" By the faith that I owe to my soul, and by the faith
that I owe to the fair Lady," said the Bishop, " never
before has there happened in the world so great a
marvel as this one." And he kissed him ten times
before that he ventured to say even so much as one
word to him.

And when that the Bishop was somewhat calmed,
then they all seated them on the ground, and they
began to demand of him that, for the love of God,
he should tell unto them all in what manner he had
saved his life, and shielded his body from danger in
the sea. Then sighing, he made answer, " Foolishly
do you marvel. Our Lady, the Holy Mary, who
holds dominion throughout the world, has sustained

me everywhere on earth, and in the depths of the
sea, and through the deep sea she has guided me
behind your boat, and by her great grace she has
brought me into port as soon as you."

"Gracious Lady, Holy Mary, aid us!" said the
Bishop. "Tell me, very fair and gentle heart, in
what manner have you escaped from the sea? What
chanced to you when you fell? When that you
vanished from sight down below there in the sea, in
that great gulf and that great abyss, the which is so
large and so deep, what befell you, and what did
you think on? The which were you, quick or dead?
In the name of God and of His gracious Mother, tell
me, very fair and gentle brother, and discover unto
me, this marvel. So greatly do I wonder at this,
that, by the Holy Mary, it seemeth to me that it
may be sorcery."

Then said the shipwrecked one, "Sire, wherefore
do you so greatly marvel? This is the truth.
The Queen, the pure Virgin, who has saved every

one, is well able to save a man from the fire of Hell."

And the Bishop made answer, " This is not to be doubted. Foolish is he who doubts that the holy Mother Mary, who has given life to the world, and who is of so very high estate, can do her pleasure everywhere. But we would know all, by what course, by what means, and in what way, and how, the Mother of the gentle King who errs not, has saved you, and brought you hither. Many days and many nights have passed by since that, in my sight, you fell in there, and forsooth you cannot have eaten there."

" Eaten ? " he straightway made answer. " It seems to me that I have but just eaten."

" But just now ? " said the Bishop. " By the Holy Father, brother, more than a fortnight has passed."

" So help me God," said he, " never until the morrow shall I either thirst or hunger."

Then the Bishop made answer, " By my soul and body, you have been in a good place.  Tell me, for God's sake, what befell you, and what happened unto you, when that you fell in ? "

" Why this," he answered, weeping.  " When that I fell in, I cried out to the sweet Mother of God, and besought her from the bottom of my heart, for in nowise could I utter a word.  With such violence did I fall, that I called not upon any Saint, and not even upon God did I call.  But upon the Holy Mary, the sweet Mother of the King of Glory, whom I have always in remembrance, I ceased not to call from the time when that I fell into the sea,—the which is so vast and so deep that I know not how to tell of it or to set it forth,—until that I was come to the bottom of it.  And the gracious Maiden, who is the Queen of the world, came straightway to me in the hideous and deep sea, and so greatly did the sweet Lady cover me with her mantle (2), that, upon my soul, never after did I fear the sea, or any living thing. And through the fearful and dark sea, the right blessed Maiden, the sweet glorious Virgin, has, under her mantle, and with great care, guided me to land, and by her might has brought me hither, as you can see."

And the Bishop, weeping, exclaimed, " Sweet Lady, Holy Mary, noble, holy, and worthy Queen, pitiful and gracious Maiden, very sweet Mother of the King Jesus, may you be glorified! No one is there, in heaven or on earth, who truly seeks you, who does not receive aid in all things."

Well is this shown by this miracle of the ship-wrecked one, the which I have related.

And longwhiles, and with much earnestness, did they, and all who were there, worship with many tears the Mother of the King to whom all cry. Of this miracle there is no more to relate, either from my books, or of myself.

# NOTES

## OF THE DROWNING MAN DELIVERED

1. A bird was often used as a symbol of the soul, as may be seen, amongst other instances, in the "Book of the Dead," where, as representing the soul, it is found hovering over the mummied body. (Papyrus No. 10,470, B. Mus.) In Egyptian writings and inscriptions, it is used as the *hieroglyph* of the soul.

The recent excavations in Crete have brought to light representations of the dove figuring in primitive Cretan art. From thence it was introduced into Cyprus, Sicily, and the Syrian coast, about 1500 B.C., when the Cretans founded Gaza. It is from this Cretan cult, thus introduced into Syria, that the dove, whether used as an emblem of the Holy Spirit, or, by extension, of spirit or soul generally, has found its way into Christian art, in which a white dove, though more generally made use of to ypify the Holy Spirit, is not infrequently found as an emblem of the human soul.

In ancient art, the soul is sometimes also represented by a butterfly escaping from the mouth of the dead, and sometimes, as on the Greek *lekythi* which were buried with the dead, by a tiny figure flitting across space. On Greek gems it may be seen represented by a full-grown figure, which Hermes, as the conductor of souls, leads to the Shades. In Byzantine, Mediæval, and early Renaissance art, the conception of the soul is frequently expressed in the form of a little child, though this form, which was such a favourite one in Christian art, dates from before the Christian era. The soul in the form of a butterfly, is also found in Chinese stories, as well as in Japanese stories of Chinese origin. The most wonderful endeavour to express the soul in words, is to be found in the *Paradiso*, canto xxx., where Dante, in a vision the most glorious that man has ever recorded, or perhaps ever seen, likens the souls of the Blessed to pearls and rubies and topazes, which he sees issuing like living sparks from out a river of light (e vidi lume in forma di riviera . . . di tal fiumana usciam faville vive). But however poetical or sublime any attempts to visualise the soul, either to our mental or our bodily eyes, may be, the results of such attempts must for ever remain mere hieroglyphs.

2. The strange affinity between the ideas underlying the wonderful stories of magic carpets, cloaks, and caps, and the motive of the protecting mantle of the Virgin, suggests for the latter an Eastern origin. The incident of Odysseus saving himself from his storm-shattered raft with the " Veil imperishable " which the sea-goddess Leucothea had given him to wind about him before casting himself into the sea, is evidently only another variant of this same idea of supernatural intervention, and leads one to the conclusion that there existed, in the remote past, a common stock of legends and myths, which poets and chroniclers from time to time adapted to their own special environment, just as, later, we find them transformed to suit Christian teaching. As connected with the Virgin, the motive referred to is frequently found in art, though rarely in literature. When the Virgin is represented holding out her

mantle on either side, with her votaries, be they many or few, seeking shelter within its folds, she is known as the Virgin of Mercy. Many pictures in which she is thus represented were votive offerings, made after, or in the hope of averting, some calamity. The idea of symbolising protection by the enveloping folds of a garment, seems to have appealed to the early artists. In many representations of the " Liberal Arts," the figure of *Grammar* is seen personified as a woman with one or two children sheltering in the folds of her garment. The same idea may also be seen in personifications of *Charity*, in representations of the " Theological Virtues."

OF  A  JEW  WHO  TOOK  IN
PLEDGE  THE  IMAGE  OF  OUR
LADY

Of a Jew who took in pledge the
Image of Our Lady.

# OF A JEW WHO TOOK IN PLEDGE THE IMAGE OF OUR LADY (1)

VERILY I find it recorded that, on a time, there lived in the great city of Byzantium a citizen who held Our Lady in high honour. He was rich, and of great name, for that he had possessions and great repute. And so largely did he give away for to increase his renown, and so much did he give himself up to hurtful pleasures, that ere long his great possessions were all consumed, and his affairs were come to such a pass, that he was constrained to sell his lands. Ne'ertheless, so large of heart was he, that never could poverty make him miserly or mean. And always, without ceasing, he made ample and goodly cheer, and gave away more and more, here, and there, and everywhere. And so long as he could borrow, the thought of poverty troubled him not. But at last all his friends grew weary of him when they perceived that he too much exposed himself to the danger of penury, and that to no one did he repay aught, for he who borrows, and repays naught, and is paid naught by his debtors, soon loses his credit, even though he be King of France.

And the good citizen was much an-angered, and knew not what to do or to say when he perceived that his creditors beset him, and that his friends wholly failed him. Great grief and sorrow had he, and much shame and distress and sadness, when he could no longer command that by the which he could maintain his liberality, or do good to the poor. Whiles that he had wealth, and possessed gold and silver, he was very generous to poor folk But Dame Fortune assailed him with such rancour, and caused him so much shame and hurt, that he had naught

left to bestow on himself or on others. And in
nowise did she show him favour, but turned her
countenance away from him.

And the unhappy citizen knew not what to do,
for none would look at him, and those to whom
he had done most good mocked at him.   Such,
without doubt, is the way of the world when that
Fortune casts any honest man to the bottom of her
wheel (2).   And those to whom he had given most aid
defamed him, and regarded him as viler than a dog,
and those who in his time of success had held him in
regard and esteemed him, scoffed at him and treated
him with contempt.   Holy Writ, forsooth, condemns
him who puts his trust in man.   Certes, so scant and
so rare is loyalty, that children neglect their father,
and the daughter fails the mother.   Foolish is he who
ruins himself for others, for as soon as ruin overtakes
him, all say to him, " Begone."

And then the citizen, who had such longwhile
been so esteemed and so sought after, perceived that

he was despised, and he saw well that no longer had he in the town either relation or friend who regarded him other than as a vile dog.

And, perchance because God willed it, he knew not what to say or what to do, or how to seek counsel in his difficulty. And all in despair, he straightway went in anger to a Jew, the richest in the city.

"Jew," said he, "verily all my daughters and my sons, and all my friends and those in this world to whom I have done most good, have wholly failed me. I am bereft of my wealth, and foolish and luckless have I been in that I have squandered it on these clerks and laymen who now forsake me. I am a merchant of great experience, and if you will lend me of your wealth, so much do I reckon to add to it, that never do I look to beg of others, and such increase shall I make of it, that for this all will hold me in greater esteem."

"Since you have been so liberal," said the Jew,

" forthwith shall you have ample, if that I can have surety for it."

Then he made answer, " Good, kind friend, all my kinsmen and my friends have so cast me off, that none have any care for me, albeit I have maintained all by my liberality and my work.  No surety can I have of any kinsman, and now no friends have I.  No bail or guarantee can I have, however much endeavour I may make, and truly I can have neither pledge nor surety.  But I now swear on my faith that to the very day I will make repayment unto you of your loan."

" Then naught can you have," said the Jew, " for I fear me that you will make default in your covenant."

" Good, kind friend," he made answer, " since I cannot furnish either surety or bond, take in plight, I pray of you, my Creator, Jesus Christ, the King of Heaven, the God of Gods, in whom I put my trust.  I swear to you, good brother Jew, by God and by His gentle and dear Mother, that if so it be that you have not your money again on such day as you shall name, I will be your bondsman in such wise, that, on my oath, I will become your serf. And so much shall I be in your power, that you can sell me in the market-place like as a beast."

And the Jew who, in his heart, much coveted and desired his bondage, laughing, made answer, " In nowise do I believe that Jesus Christ, the son of Mary, whom our forefathers crucified on a piece of wood, was God. But forasmuch as He was so holy a man, and a prophet of so great renown, if so it be that in His name you give me your pledge to serve me all your life if you fail me in your covenant, without demur will I accept it."

" On my soul," said he, " right well have you spoken. Let us repair to the church of Our Lady, the glorious Mother of God."

And they took with them to the church many Christians and Jews. And many clerks and laymen

there heard them covenant and make bargain. And
forthwith the unhappy citizen kneeled down before
the image. And he wept, and shed hot tears, and
wetted all his face, because of the distress the
which drove him forth. And the wretched man
knew not what to do. But he cast all his trouble upon
God, and, weeping, he besought of His very precious
Mother that she would deign to deliver him from
misery and from servitude.

And he was sorely troubled in mind concerning
the matter. And when that he had made prayer unto
Our Lady, he sprang up and said, " On my soul,
friend Jew, here is my pledge. Through this child
and this image, I give you Jesus Christ for pledge.
He has created me and fashioned me, and He war-
rants me this money. No better pledge can you ever
have, so help me God."

And he placed the hand of the Jew in that of
the child, and straightway, whilst with tearful eyes
he humbly remained kneeling, he uttered the pledge

and the oath aloud in the presence of all. "Good Lord God, who art beyond measure mighty and gracious and powerful, with clasped hands I now, through the mediation of your sweet Mother, beseech of you, very loving and benign Father, that, if it so chance that from any cause I am unable to make return to him of this money to the very day, you will extend your goodness in such wise as to redeem your pledge to him that if for but a single day I make default in my oath, the which I swear on your image and the Saints, his slave shall I be as long as my life dures."

Then he rose up, his face all wet with tears, and the Jew, without tarrying, made loan to him of a large sum to use as he would. And no longer had he desire to amuse himself. Well did he perceive that too much had he done this. He who has been scalded, dreads hot water. He knew well that of a surety he who possesses naught is much despised.

And the heart of the good citizen, whom God had

in His keeping, throbbed, and fluttered, and leaped when that he was in possession of the money. And he laded a ship on the coast with divers merchandise of the which he had much knowledge, and to God, in whom he put his trust, he commended himself and his goods. And with sails set, he passed over the sea, and trafficked in his wares in many lands. And so much did the adventure prosper, that, ere the year had passed by, he was delivered from poverty. God increased his substance wheresoever he employed it. And when he perceived that he had much riches, in nowise was he sparing of his possessions. Freely did he make distribution of them for the sake of God, who plenteously bestows all good things.

And in a little while he became rich, and acquired one possession after another, and multiplied his estate, and so much did he prosper, and so much did he win, and such wealth did he come to possess, that he knew not how to reckon it up, so says the story the which records this.

And in order to make gain, he went into many strange lands. And one day passed, and another came, and he thought not on the time when he must make return unto the Jew of the money of the which he had made so great increase. Albeit, the time was well-nigh passed, but he remembered it not until there was but one day left, and by chance he bethought him of it whiles that he was on the sea. And he was like to die when he had it in remembrance. "Ah! Sweet Lady of the King of Glory, gentle, gracious Maiden, what, alas, can this unhappy being do?" said he. And into such grief was he plunged, that he clenched his fists, and beat his breast, and gnashed and set his teeth, and after a while he fell to the ground in a swoon. And his attendants came together, and all around him they cried out and wept for verily did they believe that he was quite dead. And greatly did they mourn and grieve, for not a word could they get from him, and, in great sorrow and trouble, no pulse or breathing could they perceive in him.

And when that he was recovered from his swoon, he threw himself on the ground in prayer, and long-whiles did he weep and sigh, and so troubled was he, that he knew not what to say. " Alas, unhappy mis-chance!" said he. " What a foolish merchant have I been! How grievously has misfortune overtaken me! How has the Evil One deceived me! How has he bewitched me, in that I have not better borne in mind the day! Deeply is it graven on my heart that I gave for pledge Jesus Christ, and His very sweet and dear Mother. Alas! truly ought I to be downcast, and to be sad and sorrowful at heart, for neither by day nor by night have I bethought me to discharge and make payment of this great sum, the which to-day makes me so disquieted. Dis-quieted, indeed! I have a right to be so! If that a bird were to wing its flight on the instant, not in thirty days, or in forty, would it arrive at Byzantium. Alack! Alack! I have fallen into bondage. Truly have I brought shame upon all my kindred. Of very little worth is great wealth since I am thus bound and enslaved."

And the good citizen made great dole, and much did he sigh and make lament. And when that he had grieved much, and made great plaint, and had much tormented him, as if the Holy Ghost inspired him, he regained his courage, and said, " Wherefore do I make lament ? I ought to be comforted in that He who has power over all is given in pledge for me. He has taken the matter upon Himself. No longer does it trouble me. I owe the money, and He will make payment of it, and thus, by His goodness, will He make recompense for me. On the morrow I ought to make return of the money if that I am to be delivered out of his hands. Even if I spent all to-day, never would this give me concern. Verily, I leave all in His hands. Naught else can I see to do, such great misfortune would befall me in the end without His help. He is pledged to this, and of a surety He

will release me from it, and none other quittance
can I have."

And without more ado, the citizen straightway
took a strong casket, and within it he placed the
money the which he had to restore to the Jew.   And
without waiting for the morrow, he cast it into the
sea, and, weeping, committed it to the care of the
great Lord and God who has all the world in His
keeping, and who governs and has charge over the
earth and the sea.   And He who is of such high
estate that naught that He would do is difficult or
impossible or troublesome unto Him, all the night
so directed the casket, the which was worth many
besants, that it was borne more than a thousand
leagues ere the day dawned.   And to the very day,
the casket arrived at Byzantium.

And as God willed it, it so chanced that the rich
and wealthy Jew who had lent this money was
dwelling by the sea-shore, and one of his varlets

rose early on a summer's morn, and saw the casket, the which had just arrived, close to the shore. And he leaped into the sea all clothed, and thought to seize it, but he failed, for the casket pitched and tossed whensoever he thought to lay hold on it. And greatly desirous was he to possess himself of it, but he could not stretch out his hand far enough to reach it. And it seemed to say, "Begone! I belong not to you."

And he went straightway to his master, who dwelt right on the shore, and anon the casket came straight to him. And verily he thought that it said, "Receive me, good Sir Jew. God makes quittance to you for the citizen, and henceforth he is free."

Then the Jew carried the casket as quickly as he could within his house. And when that he had emptied it of the great fortune, he secreted it at the foot of his bed so that none might know aught concerning it.

And he found a letter in the which he read that

ere long the citizen, who had journeyed much, and had travelled in many lands, would return to Byzantium with many ships laden with great wealth. And his friends and his acquaintances had great joy and gladness on account of this, and right seemly and pleasing was the festival the which they held in the city in honour of him. And they were all stirred with joy, and both clerks and layfolk made rejoicing over it.

And when the Jew heard of the welcome the which was accorded to the citizen, he forthwith went to him. And he questioned him much, and held much speech with him, and at last he spoke to him of the money, to the end that he might see if he was able to make repayment.

And when that he had greeted him heartily and made merry, laughing, he took him by the arm. And he shook his head, and said to him, " Good Christian, Good Christian." And at first the citizen smiled, and then he said, " What means this ? "

" On my oath it means that, of my fortune, I made

loan unto you of more than a bushel of my deniers, the which you were to render to me again by a day which has passed. And the covenant holds that if you made default for but one day, ever after would you be my serf, and if you depart from this, in nowise shall I set the value of two ears of corn upon you, or on your faith or your belief."

And he who put his trust in God made answer to the Jew, " Naught do I owe you. All that I owed you, that have I paid unto you in full."

Then the Jew, who was very shrewd, said, " Ah ! I have at hand plenty of witnesses. Never have you made payment of aught of it. Naught is there surprising in this."

" Enough proof of payment and of quittance shall I have," said he. " You would make me altogether in ill humour if that I had not such good security, and if you will come to the church where the pledge was taken, right well do I think to show you proof of mine acquittance."

And they, and so many others, went together to the church, that they quite filled it.

And the citizen, who had put all his hope in God, and who was very firm in his trust, kneeled very humbly on the pavement, with folded hands, before the image of Our Lady. And, sighing, he besought and prayed of her with all his heart, and with all his soul, that she would beseech of her gracious Son to hearken unto him. And then he cried with a loud voice, and thus addressed the Lord Jesus Christ. " As verily as you are the true son of God, bear witness for me to this Hebrew of the truth. Very God, very God, for the glory of your name, declare whether or not I have made discharge to him of this loan."

And the image made answer in these very words. " Certes, sure evidence is there against him that you have paid him right well to the day all that you have had of him. Of a truth, in witness of this the casket from the which he took the money of the which I made payment to him for you, is yet hidden under his bed."

And when the Jew heard the wonder, he was affrighted and astonished, and he knew not what to say or what to do. And by the will and grace of the Holy Ghost, that very day he became a Christian, and was baptized, and thenceforth he was very steadfast in the faith.

And each year, by good custom, for to call to mind this marvel, they had grand caroles, and much jollity and high festival, and much ceremony, in Byzantium, the great city the which Constantine, who was noble of heart, afterwards called Constantinople.

# NOTES

## THE JEW

1. The date assigned to this story is the tenth century, and the church in which the pledge was given is said to be that of St. Sophia, Constantinople. There are variants of the story, in some versions a crucifix taking the place of the statue of the Virgin, and in others the image on the crucifix bowing its head to bear witness between the Jew and the Christian. This latter idea was probably the outcome of the poetical legend told of St. Gualberto before he became a monk of St. Miniato, Florence, and the founder of the Order of Vallombrosa, who, having forgiven an enemy whom he had meant to slay, threw himself before a crucifix in the church of St. Miniato, near to which the encounter had taken place, and, whilst praying for mercy inasmuch as he had shown mercy, fancied he saw the image on the crucifix bow in assent. This legend is still kept in remembrance in the church by a picture, over one of the altars, representing the miracle, though the traditional crucifix itself is jealously guarded in the church of the Trinità, at Florence, which belongs to the Vallombrosan Order.

2. The *Wheel*, as typical of change of fortune, seems to have appealed very forcibly to the mediæval *mind*, just as, for decorative purposes, it appealed to its *eye*. It is constantly

made use of, both in Literature and in Art, as an emblem of the instability of all worldly glory, as well as an emblem of the various phases of man's life. In some illuminated MSS. the latter idea is to be found represented by little figures between the spokes, beginning with an infant, and ending with a tomb. A fine example of this may be seen in a thirteenth century Psalter in the British Museum.

# OF OUR LADY OF ROC-
AMADOUR

*Of the taper which descended
on the viol of the minstrel
before the Image of Our Lady*

# OF OUR LADY OF ROC-AMADOUR

SO many miracles, and so many wondrous deeds, did the gentle Mother of the Creator perform at the church of Roc-Amadour, that a very large book is written thereon, and ofttimes have I read in it a very pleasing miracle, which I find there, of a minstrel, a layman, the which I will recount, so as, if may be, to cause the graciousness of Our Lady to be understood of all.

There was in the land a minstrel who sang right gladly the lay of the Mother of the Saviour when that he came to her sanctuaries. He was a minstrel of great renown, and had for name Peter de Siglar. And he went, it seems, on a pilgrimage to Roc-Amadour (1), where ofttimes many folk meet together.

And there he found many pilgrims who were come from distant lands, and who were keeping high festival.

And when that he had ended his orisons, he took up his viol. And he touched the strings with his bow, and caused the viol to resound. And as he did this, all, both clerks and laymen, forthwith came around him. And when Peter saw that all paid attention, and hearkened unto him, so well did he play, that verily he thought that his viol longed to speak. And when that he had humbly saluted the Mother of God, and had longwhiles given praise unto her with his whole heart, and had bowed low before her image, he exclaimed in a loud voice, " Ah ! Mother of the King who has created all, most gracious Lady, if aught that I say is in anywise pleasing unto you, I entreat of you to make gift to me, for recompense, of one of those tapers, of the which you have so many around you up there that never anywhere have I seen more. Lady, who art peerless and with-

out equal, send me one of your beautiful tapers to
make merry at my supper. As God sees me, naught
beside do I ask of you."

And Our Lady, the Holy Mary, who is the fountain
of all mercy, and the source and channel of goodness,
duly heard the words of the minstrel, and straightway,
without delay, and in the sight of all, she caused a
very beautiful and fair taper to descend on to the viol.

And a monk, who was named Girard, and who was
very churlish and surly, and was at that time in
charge of the church and kept watch over these things,
like a man full of ill-will, regarded the miracle as
folly. "Away with him," said he. "He is a sorcerer, a deceiver, and a knave." And he seized the
taper, and replaced it up above, and made it fast.

And the minstrel, who had good sense, perceived
that the monk was an-angered and foolish, and because
of this he opposed him not, for well did he understand and perceive that Our Lady had heard him.
And so much did he rejoice over this in his heart,

that he wept for very joy. Without ceasing did he think on the Mother of God, and give her much thanks in his heart for her very great courtesy.

And once again he took up the viol, and looked towards the image, and so well did he sing and play, that no sequence or litany was there that could be listened unto with greater pleasure. And the beautiful and new taper again descended on to his viol, and the miracle was seen of five hundred.

And when that the foolish and frenzied monk, whose head was full of what had happened, again saw the taper descend, he jostled and pushed the folk more than any stag or roe or goat. And so put out was he, that he could scarce utter a single word, and, in great anger and rage, he threw back his cowl, and said to the minstrel, " Well may I be assured that only one who is half-witted would fix his taper thus."

And much did he marvel at that which he saw, and he counted it as exceeding wonderful. Never in all his life, said he, had he seen such magic.

And full many a time did he accuse the minstrel of being a sorcerer, and, inflamed with anger and rage, he once more seized the taper, and angrily set it up again, and replaced it very firmly, and secured it well. And he said to the minstrel, " Right well am I assured, though never will it be made known, that it was not that sorcerer, Simon Magus, the magician, who made it to descend from up there."

But forsooth the minstrel, who everywhere had seen many foolish and many wise men, was in nowise disturbed by this. So patiently did he endure the rage and ill-humour of the monk, that he was in nowise discouraged. Naught did he take to heart of all that the foolish monk had said, but he began over again his song and his melody. Well knew he that Our Lady would give a good ending to the matter if that she deemed his song worthy to please her. And as he played his viol, he sighed and wept. And he sang, and made supplication in his heart. And silently he besought the Mother of God that, of her goodness, she would hearken unto him again, and that, to make the miracle the more manifest, she would at least once more cause the fair taper, the which the angry monk, who was so foolish and so mad, had twice foolishly snatched as it were out of his hands, to come back again.

And around him there was a great multitude, who were astonished and excited at the miracle which they had beheld. And they all marvelled at it, and signed them with the cross, and pointed to the taper the which had already descended twice. And Peter's fingers were not idle or slothful on his viol, but in suchwise did he sing and play before the image of Our Lady, that the music, the which his viol gave forth, made many hearts to weep for pity. And with such right goodwill did he sing and play, that the sound went up to God. And now, as we read, the taper descended a third time to the minstrel whom God comforted, and thrice did Our Lady, who understood him better than did the monk, and who

was very much more gracious than the angry monk
who was surprised and astonished at the tumult,
present it. And every one cried out, " Ring the
bells, ring the bells ! Never has there chanced such
a wondrous miracle, and never will such an one
chance again ! "

And the clerks, and laymen, and all, held high
festival in the church, and so many bells were set
ringing, that not even could God's thunder be heard.
On the faith of my soul, a hard heart must he have
had who was not moved with compassion when that
he saw the minstrel offer the taper on the altar as
a thank-offering to God and Our Lady. He was
neither mad nor presumptuous, but was courteous,
noble-hearted, and wise. And as long as his life
dured, every year, so I find in the book, he brought to
Roc-Amadour a very beautiful candle of a pound's
weight. And it delighted him to serve God in this
wise as long as he lived.

And never after did he enter any church but that

he forthwith played on his viol songs and lays of Our Lady.

And when that it pleased God that his end should come, he attained unto the glory of Heaven, and through the mediation of Our Lady, whom he joyfully honoured in song, and to whom he gave a taper each year at Roc-Amadour, his soul went up to God.

# NOTE

## LADY OF ROC-AMADOUR

1. The pilgrimage to the shrine of our Lady of Roc-Amadour is one of the most ancient in France, and is said to date from the third century, A.D. The name of Roc-Amadour (Department Lot), comes from " Roche de St. Amadour," the rocky retreat of a Saint of that name, who, according to tradition, lived in the time of the Apostles, and retired to this spot amongst the mountains in order to devote his life to the worship of a statue of the Virgin which he had himself carved. At whatever date this saintly person may have lived (and as to which there is some doubt), the shrine of Roc-Amadour was already held in veneration in the reign of Charlemagne, and, by the middle of the twelfth century, had acquired great celebrity, and it was at about that time that the hero of the present story, Peter de Siglar, a renowned troubadour, went to the sanctuary, and that the wondrous miracle of the taper befell.

" BETHINK you, gentle Lady, of your very great grace, to grant a good life, and a good end, to all those, clerks and laymen, dames and maidens, who bear with this book, and hold it in honour. Aforetime, every one, alway finding pleasure in great wonderment, delighted in it, and sang and read it with joy, and since that it has so rejoiced others, each one should delight to hold it in esteem, and to carry it everywhere."

GAUTIER DE COINCI.